# A COLORIN<br># FOR PREGNAN<br># TO BE

Written by NANCY LOU STILES

Illustrated by Martin Riskin

HELLO,<br>
This is a picture of me. I made a coloring book for you.<br>
Color it when you are in the hospital.<br>
Color me . . . a Happy Color.

# A COLORING BOOK FOR PREGNANT MOTHERS TO BE

Published simultaneously in Canada by
Encore Sales Inc. of Downsview, Ontario.

Manufactured in the United States of America.

**IVORY TOWER PUBLISHING COMPANY, INC.**
125 Walnut Street, Watertown, Massachusetts 02172
TEL: (617) 923-1111          TELEX: 955-439 Intel. Div. - ITOP

This is you. The Doctor has just told you that you are pregnant.
Now your I.U.D. becomes an I.O.U.
Color yourself . . . Surprised.

This is your husband. When your baby is born he will become a father... He is nervous ... color him... Proud!

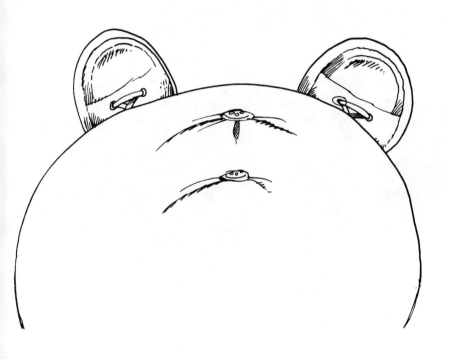

These are your feet. You had better color them now.
You won't be able to see them later.

These are your husband's parents. They are your In-Laws.
They are so happy that their son is going to be a father.
They will be your baby's Grandparents. They will think
the baby looks just like them. Color them . . . prejudiced.

These are your parents. They are very happy that you
are going to have a baby. They will be your baby's
grandparents. (If you think that's confusing, think of how
confused your baby will be.) They will say your baby
looks like them . . . color them . . . right.

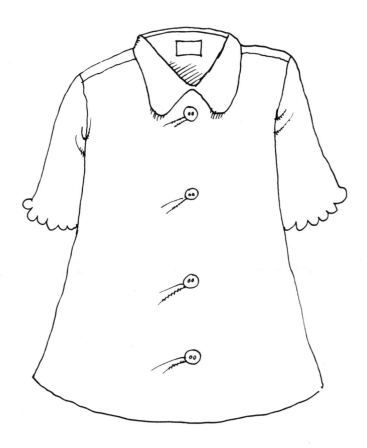

This is a Hatching Jacket. You will want to start wearing it as soon as you find out you are pregnant. Enjoy it . . . soon you will never want to see it again . . . color it . . . a boring color.

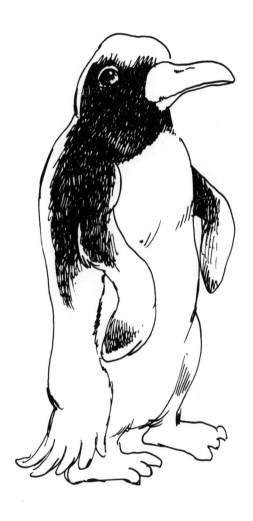

This is a penguin . . . observe him carefully. Notice he does not walk, he just waddles . . . soon you will be waddling just like him. Color the penguin . . . a slow mover.

9

Since time began women have been delivering babies . . .
Now there is a course you can take to teach you how to
deliver a baby. Your husband will want to join you in this
course. It will teach him how to react in a calm, easy,
natural manner when you start labor at home. (They don't
call it labor for nothing.) It will teach him not to get excited.
When you really do go into labor, your husband will
be very nervous. This course is a good experience.
Color the course . . . a sharing color.

These are your friends. They will ask you when your baby will be born . . . then they will ask you when you got married . . . color their fingers . . . moving.

These are the mothers of your friends. They have all
had babies. They know everything about having a baby.
They can tell you about all the trouble they had when they
were pregnant and about all the pain and suffering they
went through. Color the old wives . . . full of tales.

This is a baby shower. Your friends will surprise you and
bring you lots of nice things for your baby. All of the gifts
will be either yellow or green. None will be pink or blue . . .
You will want to dress your baby in pink or blue.
The shower will be a fun time. Color the shower . . . exciting.

When your husband takes a delivery course, they will teach
him to be part of your baby's delivery. They will teach him
to count. They will teach you how to breathe. They will
teach your husband how to pant for you when it's time for
your baby to be born. (Your husband probably already knows
how to pant for you.)
Color the course . . . Educational.
Color your husband . . . Red in the face.
Color yourself relaxed . . . and while you are coloring,
take a deep breath.

This is your house. After your baby is born, you will bring
it here to live. This will help to make your house a home.
There will be much happiness in your home. Color your
house a happy color . . . color the sun bright . . .
may the sun always shine on your home.

This is a clock. It is 7 o'clock in the morning. You may feel very strange in the morning. Don't plan any long trips. Don't plan to eat anything in the morning. By afternoon your morning sickness will wear off and you can start eating for two again. Color the clock . . . a queasy color.

This is a jar of pickles. You should have lots of pickles
around the house . . . they go well with ice cream.
Color the pickles . . . sour.

This is your favorite Ice Cream. It goes well with pickles.
Color the Ice Cream . . . Sweet.

This is a piggy bank. You can keep lots of pennies in it. You had better start filling it up now. Your baby will want to go to college soon. Color the piggy bank . . . with interest.

This is your wedding ring. Your fingers will swell up and your ring will become very tight. You should take your ring off when it becomes tight. After your baby is born the "swelling will go down" - then you can wear your ring comfortably. Color the ring . . . a tight, round color.

Now that you are pregnant, people will say you are carrying a baby. It's not true. Your baby is inside of you so you can't carry it! There will be time enough to carry it later. Color the baby . . . weightless.

This is a pot of water. Keep it handy if you go into labor at
home call your Doctor. He will tell your husband to boil
some water. This gives him something to do, keeps him out
of the way, and keeps his mind occupied. The Doctor
will not need the water. Color the water . . . hot.

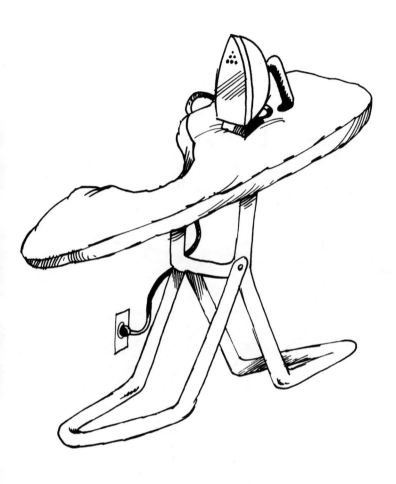

This is your ironing board. (Don't you wish it looked like this?)
You do not need to iron the diapers . . . color the ironing
board and the iron a . . . hot color.

This is your car. It will take you to the hospital when it is
time for your baby to be born. It can go very, very fast.
Don't color the car . . . fill it with gas.

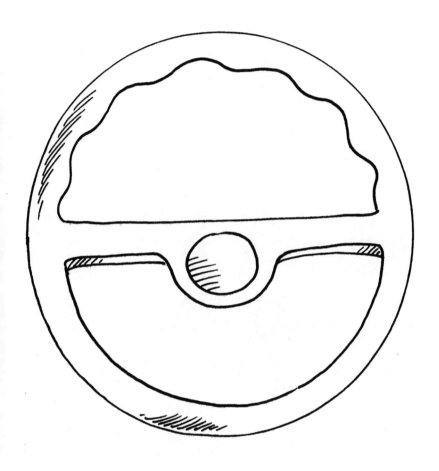

This is your steering wheel (don't you wish it looked like this?)
Color it . . . a round-about color.

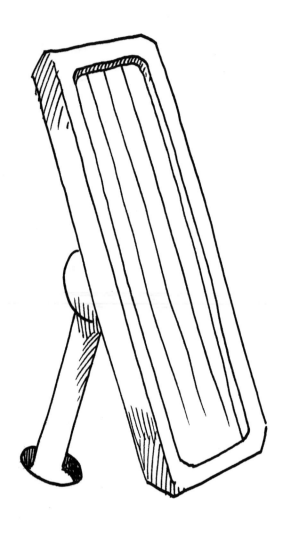

Be glad you can reach the clutch . . . you won't be able
to later. It keeps going further away.
Color the pedal . . . a distant color.

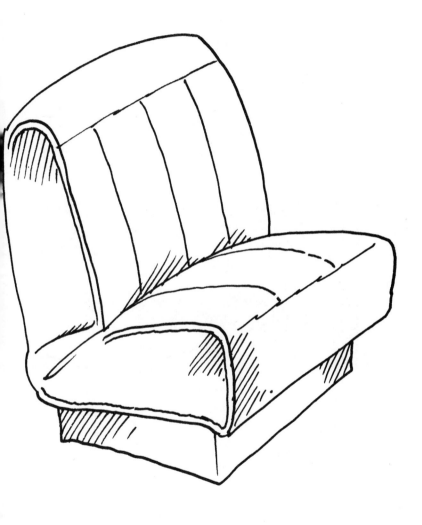

This is the seat of your car. Enjoy the empty space. Soon it will be cluttered with baby bottles, baby bags, a baby seat and a baby. Do not color the front seat, fasten the seat belt.

This is your bedroom. It is nice and neat. This is where your husband and you sleep. Color your bedroom . . . a nice . . . cozy color.

This is how your bedroom will look after your baby is born.
This is where you and your husband and your baby will sleep
(just try to sleep in it . . . just try).
It is a very cozy place - color the bedroom . . . crowded.

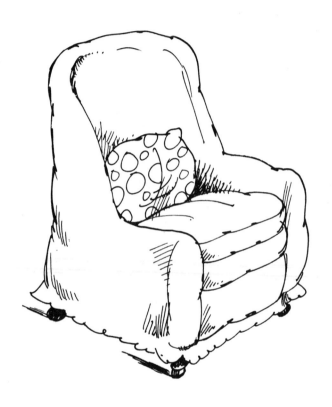

This is an easy chair (whoever named it an easy chair wasn't pregnant). Don't sit in it! It's NOT easy to get out of. Be careful when you color the chair . . . so you don't get stuck . . . in it.

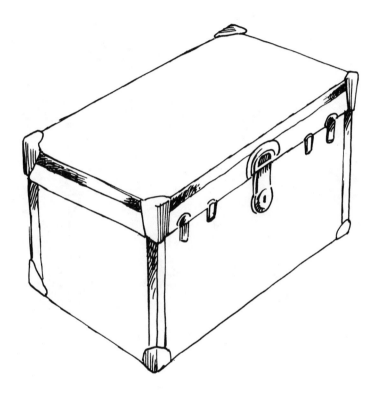

This is a trunk. After your baby is born, you will want to store
all your maternity clothes in it. This is a good idea because
soon . . . your baby will want a brother or sister to play with.
Color the trunk . . . full.

This is a scale. Your Doctor will weigh you each time you visit him. He will record your weight. You have to believe him when he says you have gained too much weight because soon you won't be able to see the scale. Color the scale . . . a HEAVY color.

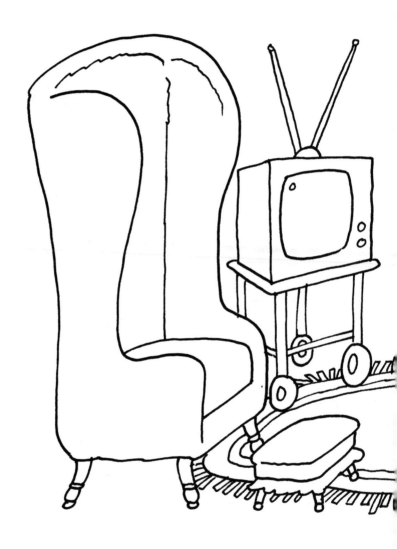

This is your 'Den'. Soon it will have a playpen, lots of blocks
and toys in it . . . it will be a playroom and not a 'Den' any
more. Color the 'Den' now . . . it may be the only
chance you get.

Be careful what medications you take. Some can make you
have more than one baby. Most people have theirs the
hard way . . . One-at-a-time.
Color the medicine a leery color.

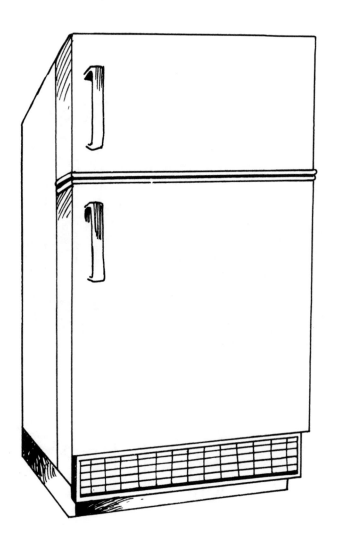

This is your refrigerator. Your husband will want to defrost it
when you are in the hospital.
Color the refrigerator . . . fattening.

This is the way to the hospital. You should practice going there . . . it usually takes 10 minutes to get there . . . your husband can get there in 5 minutes. Color the road . . . bumpy.

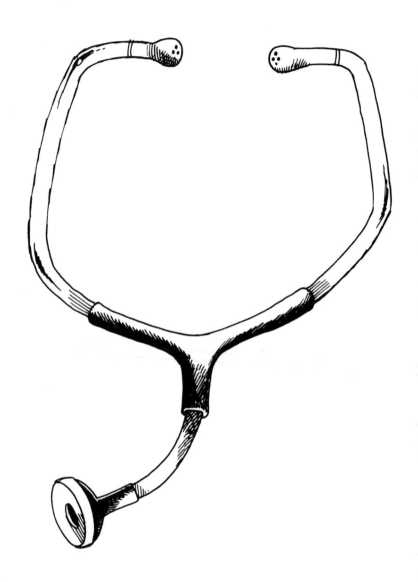

This is the Doctor's stethoscope. Your Doctor will put it on
your tummy and listen to your baby's heartbeat - it is tiny and
fast. He keeps the stethoscope in the freezer. Don't believe
him when he laughs and says that the second beat is just an
echo . . . color the stethoscope . . . a cold color.

This is your Doctor. He is a very important part of having a
baby. He is a kindly man. He says hum . . . and hum . . .
and hum . . . all those hums cost a lot of money. You should
have a lot of confidence in your Doctor. Be very comfortable
with him . . . you both have something in common . . .
this is his first baby too! Color him . . . uptight.

Your Doctor will tell you to take off all your clothes. He will
examine you all over. After this thorough examination,
he will take your blood pressure.
Color your blood pressure . . . High!

If you were very modest before the baby was born, you probably won't be afterwards. Should your Doctor meet you on the street and see your face, he probably wouldn't recognize you.
Color yourself . . . a formerly modest color.

This is your kitchen. You should come here every night at 2 a.m. just so you will get used to seeing it at 2 a.m. Do not color your kitchen . . . fix yourself a cup of coffee instead.

Soon you will feel the baby move. This feeling will bring you great joy. You will know your baby is fine by all that movement. (Couldn't your baby try out for the olympics after it is born?)
Color your baby . . . active.
Color yourself . . . content.

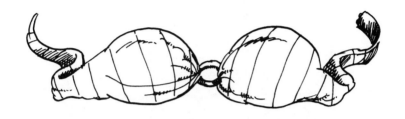

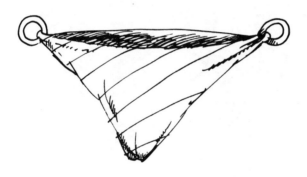

This is a bikini. Hang it up and look at it often. Remember
when you could wear it?
Next summer you can try to wear it again.
Color the bikini . . . a hopeful color.

All your friends will advise you on the advantages and disadvantages of nursing your baby. The advantage is that no one else can do it but you. The disadvantage is that no one else can do it but you.

Color this . . . a warm and tender way to nourish your baby.

Your friends' mothers will tell you all the things that can happen when your baby grows up. No wonder your friends turned out that way. Do not color them . . . their stories are colorful enough. Just ignore them.

This is you trying to lay down in bed. You will have to lay on your side or on your back. You probably have had experience laying down before, however, you may find it difficult to lay down now. After the baby is born, you can lay on your stomach again.
Color yourself . . . an uncomfortable color.

These are all the letters, brochures, and information you will
receive in the mail. Once the word is out that you are
pregnant, you and your husband will get all kinds of letters
from pro-life to family planning literature. They call
themselves "Educational". They think you want to know
what they have to say.
Color the organizations . . . Presumptuous.
Color the literature . . . Presumptuous.

This is a little kid in a supermarket. He will blurt out to everyone how fat your stomach is. If this is your first baby, you will be embarrassed. You may tell him you're fat because you eat little kids!
Color the little kid . . . Obnoxious.

When you go out in public, children will ask their mothers
and fathers how babies are made. Their mothers will try
to explain to them where babies come from. Their fathers
will tell them they came from Cleveland.
Color the parents . . . Awkward.
Color the little children . . . Inquisitive.

This is the stork. Many people believe the stork brings new babies. You do all the work and the stork gets all the credit! The truth of the matter is, the stork does not have a damn thing to do with it! These people are naive.
Color the stork . . . an innocent color.

This is the hospital. It is a very busy place. This is where
your baby will be born. There are many things going on in the
hospital. I hope they don't get you mixed up with someone
else . . . color the hospital . . . a very clean color.

This is an elevator. You will use it to get to the maternity floor.
I hope your baby isn't born in it.
Color the elevator . . . up and down.

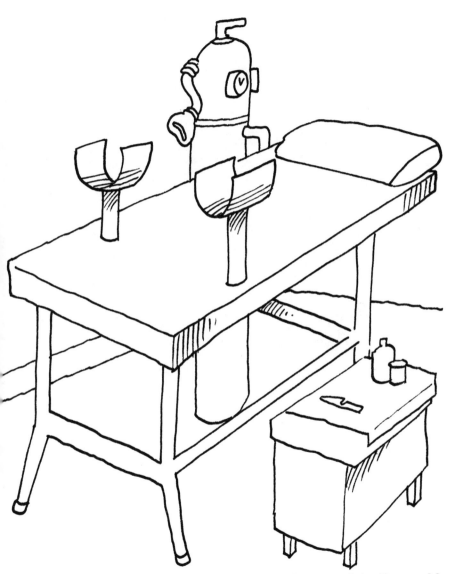

This is the Delivery Room. Your baby will come into the world in this room. Everything in this room is sterile. Do not color it unless your crayons are sterile. Your husband may come in here (even if he isn't sterile). He can watch your baby being born.

This is the nurse in the Delivery Room . . . She should have
been a football player! She will call you "Dearie" like . . .
"Turn over Dearie . . . Have we had 'our' B.M. yet Dearie? . . .
I'm just going to give you a little bee sting again Dearie" . . .
She thinks you are a pin cushion . . . color her . . . gruff.

This is the father's waiting room. This is where your husband
will wait for the baby to be born. It is a very small room.
The rug is all worn out. Color the room . . . a smokey color.

These are the flowers people send to you when you are in the
hospital. A lot of people like you and your husband because
you are nice people and nice people have nice children.
Color the flowers . . . a nice color.

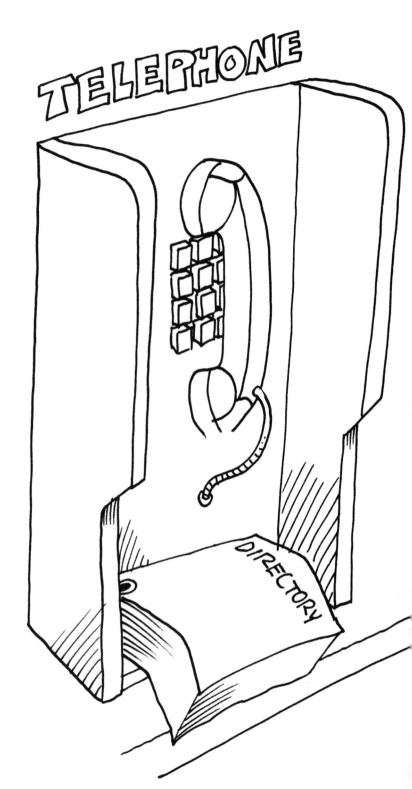

This is a telephone. Your husband will use it to call all your
relatives when your baby is born.
Color the phone . . . busy.

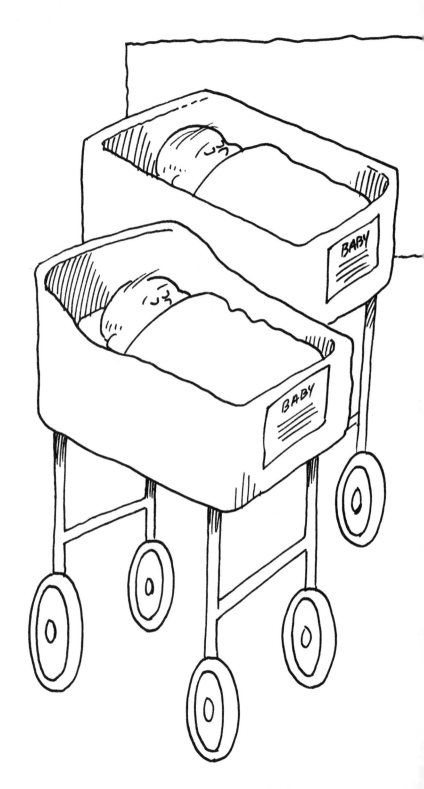

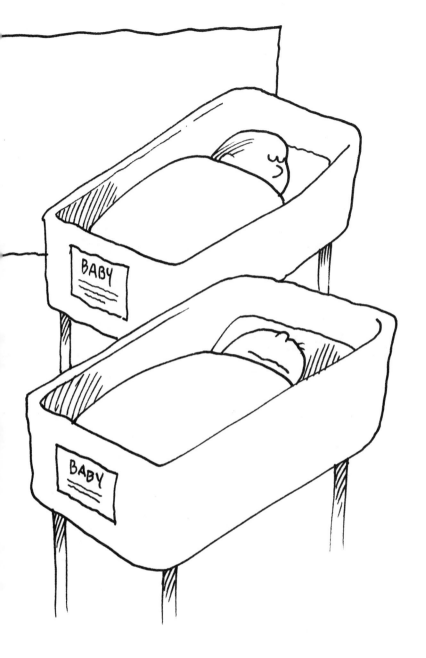

This is the nursery. It will be your baby's bedroom while it is in the hospital. Your baby will share the bedroom with lots of other babies, but the babies don't mind. The blankets are pink and blue. Color them quietly . . . so you won't . . . wake the babies.

This is the nursery nurse. She reminds you of Mrs. Santa Claus.
She takes good care of your baby. When you leave you will
want to take her home with you . . . She stays with the
hospital. Color her . . . a gentle color.

This is a baby bottle. Your baby will like the bottle. Soon you
will learn the baby can't cry and eat at the same time.
Color the bottle sterile inside. Color the milk a warm color.

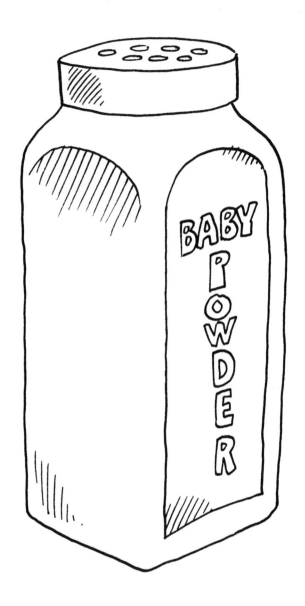

This is baby powder. It makes your baby feel nice and smell good. You will want to use it often. Don't use too much on your baby's face . . . people will tell you how pale your baby looks. The baby powder is made by Johnson & Johnson. Congratulations - you have graduated from Masters & Johnson to Johnson & Johnson.
Color the powder . . . white and fluffy.

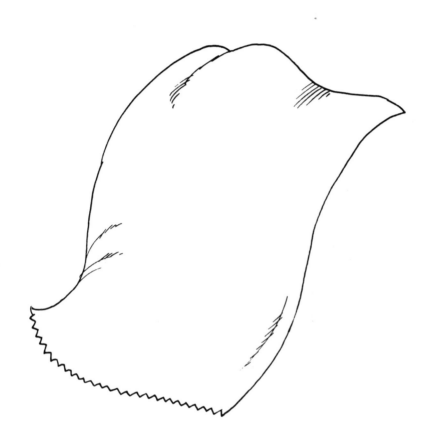

This is a diaper. It is very soft. You will become very familiar with it. Do not color it . . . Soon it will acquire a color all its own.

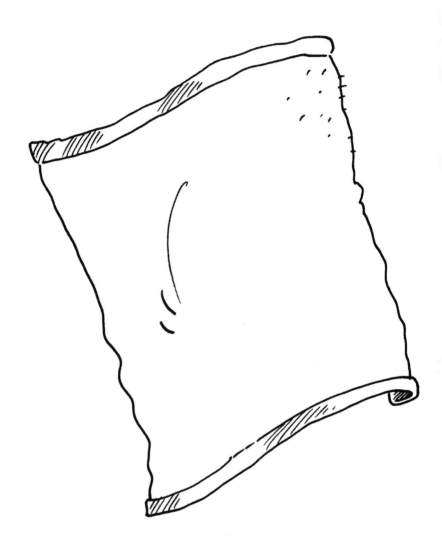

This is a baby blanket. It will be wrapped around your baby when they first bring your baby to you. If you want to know if your baby is a girl or boy, you will have to look under the blanket . . . way down under the blanket. If your baby has blue booties on, it's a boy. If your baby is wearing pink booties, it's a girl. You have to take whatever it is. There's no sending it back.
Color the baby's blanket . . . very soft.

After your baby is born, the nurse will bring you your new baby, all wrapped up like a mummy. You will unwrap your baby and look at it. The nurse will say "You're not supposed to unwrap the babies in the room". "Don't unwrap the baby" . . . you will anyway. You will want to look your baby all over! You will count all the fingers and toes and look in its mouth . . . (it has all pink teeth).

Color the nurse . . . without any heart.

Color yourself . . . content.

Color your baby . . . perfect.

Most newborn babies look very scrawny . . . Your friends
will come to see how scrawny your baby looks. Then they will
tell you how pretty your baby is.
Color your friends . . . with two faces.
Color your baby . . . beautiful.

These are your friends again. They will all come to see you
in the hospital. They will come with gifts. They will all tell
you how happy they are that your baby looks just like your
husband. Use your nose to color them . . .
because they are nosey people.

These are your parents again. Your mother is smiling. She is
so happy you are a mother to such a beautiful little baby. She
is feeling so happy. She is beaming all over. Your father is not
smiling . . . he is not sure he will like being married to a
Grandmother. Color both your parents . . . happy and proud.

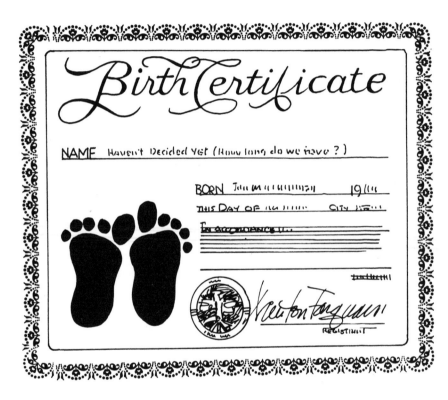

# *Birth Certificate*

NAME  Haven't Decided Yet (How long do we have ? )

BORN _____ 19__

THIS DAY OF _____ CITY ____

IN ACCORDANCE _____

REGISTRAR

This is your baby's birth certificate. It is proof that your baby
belongs to you (in case your baby was wondering) . . .
It is an important document. Color it . . . official.

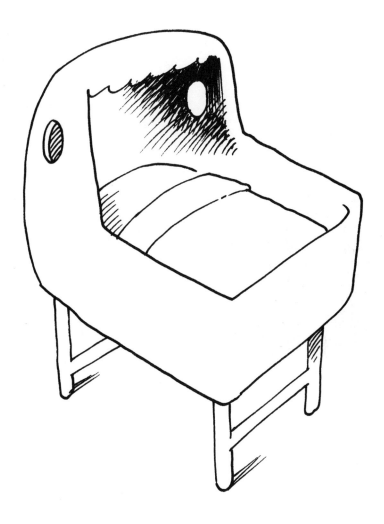

This is a bassinet. It is all frilly and lacy. It is clean and warm. It will be your baby's first bed. Soon your baby will outgrow it.
Color the bassinet . . . a soft and secure color.

This is a playpen. Your baby will not be able to get through the bars of the playpen . . . it will be a safe place for you to sit and read. Color the playpen . . . a place of isolation.

**This is your baby.**
**Do not color your baby . . . change it.**